This book belongs to

....

....

Goodword Books
1, Nizamuddin West Market, New Delhi - 110 013
email: info@goodwordbooks.com
Illustrated by Gurmeet,
Ramendranath Sarkar, Manab Bhatacharya,
Chaitali Chatterjee, Bharati Mirchandani
First published 2004   Reprinted 2008
© Goodword Books 2008
Printed in India

www.goodwordbooks.com

JUST FOR KIDS
QURAN STORIES

by

S. KHAN

Goodword**kidz**

CONTENTS

The
Treasure House

Long long ago in the lands of Egypt there lived a tribe known as the Children of Israel. Qarun or Korah was a man of the Children of Israel during the days of the Prophet Musa عليه السلام.

6

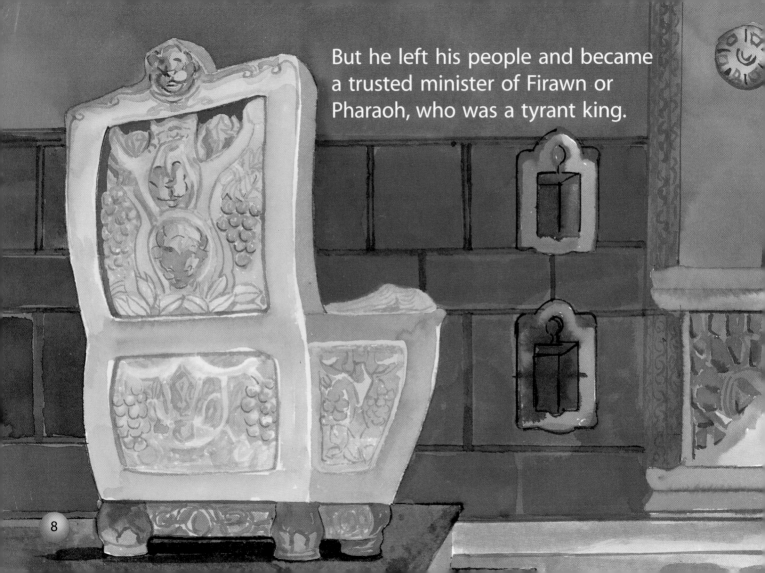

But he left his people and became a trusted minister of Firawn or Pharaoh, who was a tyrant king.

Qarun became so rich that the keys of his treasure were too heavy even for several strong men to carry.

Instead of being grateful to Allah, he chose to behave as if he was much better than others and to treat them cruelly.

12

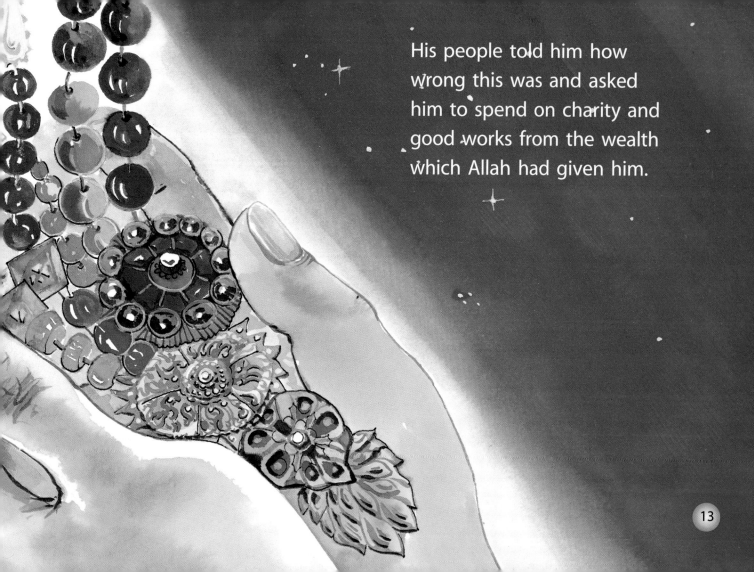

His people told him how wrong this was and asked him to spend on charity and good works from the wealth which Allah had given him.

13

But he went on as before, arguing that the wealth which he had was due to his own knowledge and cleverness. When he showed off the glitter of his great wealth, those who loved the worldly life said, "We wish we could be rich like Qarun too! Surely he is a man of great good fortune."

But those who had been given true knowledge said, "Alas for you! The reward of Allah in the Hereafter is better for him who believes and does good works, and none shall receive it except those who have borne all ills without complaint."

16

The Prophet Musa ﷺ cursed Qarun (Korah) so that Allah made the earth swallow him up along with his treasure house.

Seeing this terrible end of Qarun, those who on the day before had longed to be like him, began to say: "Behold! Allah gives much to whom He will and little to whom He pleases."

This punishment of Qarun or Korah is a great reminder to believers to be pleased with Allah and thank Him whether they be rich or poor.

Find Out More

To know more about the message and meaning of Allah's words, look up the following parts of the Quran which tell the story of Qarun—a rich man during the days of the Prophet Musa ﷺ.

Surah al-Qasas (The Story) 28:76-82

The Sleepers in the Cave

It was about A.D. 250, during the rule of a Roman King Decius (Daqyanus), that the teachings of the Prophet Isa (Jesus) ﷺ were spread throughout the region by his early followers.

The people there were idol-worshippers and the moon was treated as a god and worshipped. But seven young men of a noble family accepted the new religion in Ephesus, an ancient city near the western coast of Turkey, whose ruins can still be seen. Decius took up arms against the new converts.

Due to their fearless preaching and willingness to give up everything so as to tread the right path, they were honoured with the high status of being near to Allah.

When these young believers realised that the king's soldiers were about to capture them, they ran away from the town. They took refuge in a cave so as to escape the cruelty of the king.

As they ran, they prayed to Allah: "Our Lord! show us Your Mercy and save our lives!" They ran far into the wilderness, until they found a dark cave.

They entered it with great caution, and hoped that no one would guess that there was anyone inside. Then weeping, they all prayed to Allah for His help. Allah heard their prayers and, when they lay down to rest, He caused a miracle to happen. With His supreme power over life and death, He made them fall into a deep sleep lasting 300 years. Not once during this time did they awaken. They neither ate nor drank nor made any sound.

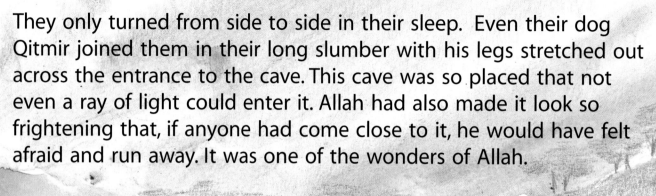

They only turned from side to side in their sleep. Even their dog Qitmir joined them in their long slumber with his legs stretched out across the entrance to the cave. This cave was so placed that not even a ray of light could enter it. Allah had also made it look so frightening that, if anyone had come close to it, he would have felt afraid and run away. It was one of the wonders of Allah.

Time passed and the town they had left changed altogether. The cruel king had died and the present king had become a believer, a follower of the message of Isa ﷺ. The king and the people were believers in Allah and were no longer idol-worshippers. During this period, Allah woke up the sleeping men. As they arose up from their long slumber and stretched their arms and legs, one of them wondered, "How long have we been here?"

They thought about it, then said, "We have been here for a day or part of a day." They did not realize that they had been sleeping there for more than three centuries! They felt very hungry, so one of them crept out of the cave to fetch something to eat. He reached the town and went to a shop to buy some food. He paid the shopkeeper with a silver coin.

The shopkeeper was amazed to see such an old coin and suspected that this man might have found some old hidden treasure. So he took him to the king, who immediately recognized that he must be one of those men who had been lost for more than three hundred years.

By order of the king, the date they were lost their names and other particulars had been engraved on a lead slab which was kept in the Royal Treasury. For this reason they also came to be known as the "men of the slab." When the slab was taken out, it was confirmed that these were the very men who had run away from the city to save their lives more than three centuries ago.

They immediately became the centre of people's devotion. The new Roman King, Theodosus, himself went on foot to see them and seek their blessings. When these young men died, a place of worship was built at their cave as a memorial.

The story tells us that those who put their entire trust in Allah, will be helped by Him in unknown ways. The story is also intended to tell us that there really is life after death.

Find Out More

To know more about the message and meaning of Allah's words, look up the following parts of the Quran which tell the story of King Dhul Qarnayan.

Surah al-Kahf 18:10-21

عَلَيْهِ السَّلَام *Alayhis Salam* 'May peace be upon him.' The customary blessings on the prophets.

The King's Magicians

The Prophet Musa عليه السلام was one of the great prophets who lived in Egypt about 4000 years ago. During his time Egypt was ruled by a tyrant king known as Firawn or Pharaoh.

Allah gave the Prophet Musa عليه السلام several miracles and asked him to go to Firawn with these signs and give His message to Firawn, who had made himself a tyrant in the land.

The Prophet Musa ﷺ threw down his staff and it turned into a big snake. Then he drew out his hand out of his armpit, and it was shining brightly. But Firawn rejected these miracles, calling them magic.

Firawn called his best magicians to outdo the Prophet Musa عليه السلام. When the magicians threw down their ropes and sticks, they looked like snakes of all sizes. Musa عليه السلام was horrified, as the snakes seemed to coil and uncoil around him.

But Allah commanded Musa ﷺ to throw down his staff. As Musa ﷺ did so, all of a sudden, it became a huge snake. What was more amazing was that it began to eat up all the other snakes one after another, until it had eaten them all up.

Everyone was wonderstruck. The magicians fell on the ground in adoration, exclaiming, "We believe in the Lord of Musa and Harun!"

The people who followed Firawn wanted him to kill Musa ﷺ. One of his follower's was Qarun (or Korah) he was very rich and had lots of treasure. But when Musa ﷺ prayed against him, Qarun's house with all his treasures sank into the earth.

Firawn was not able to harm the Prophet Musa علیه السلام. But he soon redoubled his torment on the Children of Israel.

When the tyranny of Firawn became unbearable, Allah guided the Prophet Musa عليه السلام to move out of Egypt with the entire tribe of the Children of Israel.

But Firawn pursued the caravan. As the Prophet Musa علیه السلام reached the shore of the Red Sea, the army of Firawn came very near to crushing the Children of Israel.

59

But due to a miracle of Allah, the sea split in two halves
and the caravan safely reached the other side the sea.
Firawn and his mighty army wanted to punish the
Prophet Musa ﷺ and his people. They also set their feet
on the special path created by Allah for the Children of
Israel. But as the army reached in the middle of the sea,
the sea waves fell on them and everyone was drowned.

The Prophet Musa عليه السلام and the
Children of Israel thanked Allah for
saving them from the tyrant king,
Firawn.

With patience and trust in
Allah, believers can
overcome any hardship
they face in their lives.

Find Out More
To know more about the message and meaning of Allah's
words, look up the following parts of the Quran which tell
the story of the Prophet Musa عليه السلام.
    Surah al-Araf 7:109-126, Surah al-Shuara 26:52-67

عليه السلام Alayhis Salam 'May peace be upon him.'
The customary blessings on the prophets.

The Morals
of Believers

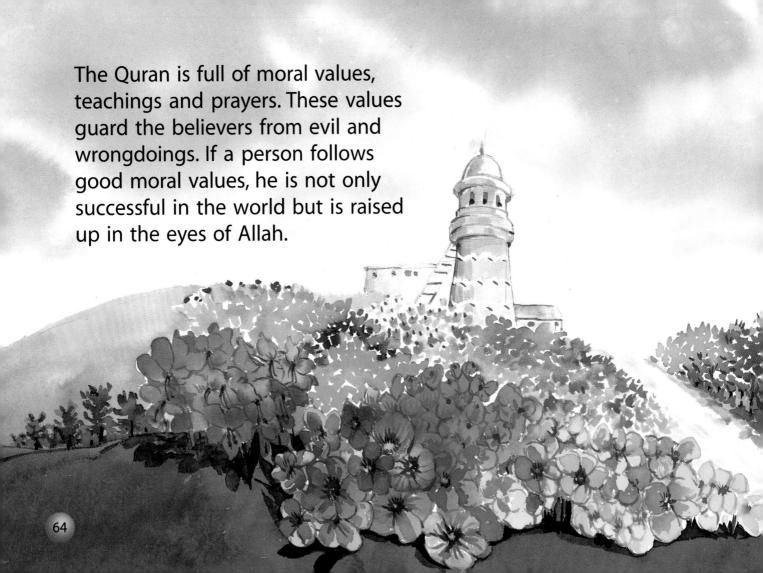

The Quran is full of moral values, teachings and prayers. These values guard the believers from evil and wrongdoings. If a person follows good moral values, he is not only successful in the world but is raised up in the eyes of Allah.

Some of the moral values which the Quran reminds the believers to practise are given in the following pages. The believers are thankful to Allah. They are diligent in their prayers. The believers are thankful to their parents. They respect their parents and elders and avoid profane talk.

Believers give
alms to the poor.
They spend their
wealth for the
cause of Allah.

67

Believers are trustworthy.
They keep their promises.
They guard their chastity.

69

Believers do not slander.
They are not mean.
Neither are they proud,
nor they scold or
make fun of others.
Believers are humble,
kind and courteous.

70

When believers become angry, they forgive. They do not behave as if they are better than others and they do not complain. Believers do not feel hatred or jealousy. They pardon those who harm them.

Believers are moderate
and avoid luxurious
living and greed.

74

Believers always remain patient if any hardship befalls on them. They do not talk rudely to others or backbite or hurt them with nicknames.

The believers do not tell lies. They are truthful and trustworthy. They always speak the truth.

May Allah help us all to possess good moral values. Amin.

Find Out More
To know more about the message and meaning of Allah's words, look up the following parts of the Quran which tell the story of Uzayr and his donkey.

Surah al-Baqarah 2:259

A Unique Miracle

The Prophet Isa (Jesus) ﷺ was born in a town called Bayt Lahm (Bethlehem), five miles south-west of Jerusalem. He grew up in Nasiriya (Nazareth). One day his disciples asked him whether his Lord could send down a table spread with food from the heavens.

'Go in fear of Allah,' warned Isa ﷺ,
'if you are true believers.'

But they insisted and in answer to the Prophet Isa's prayer, angels brought down a table spread with delicious food—a special miracle quite different from all others.

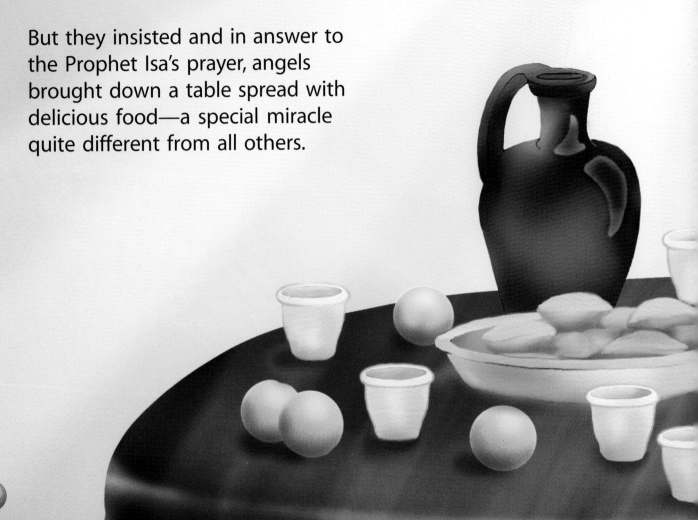

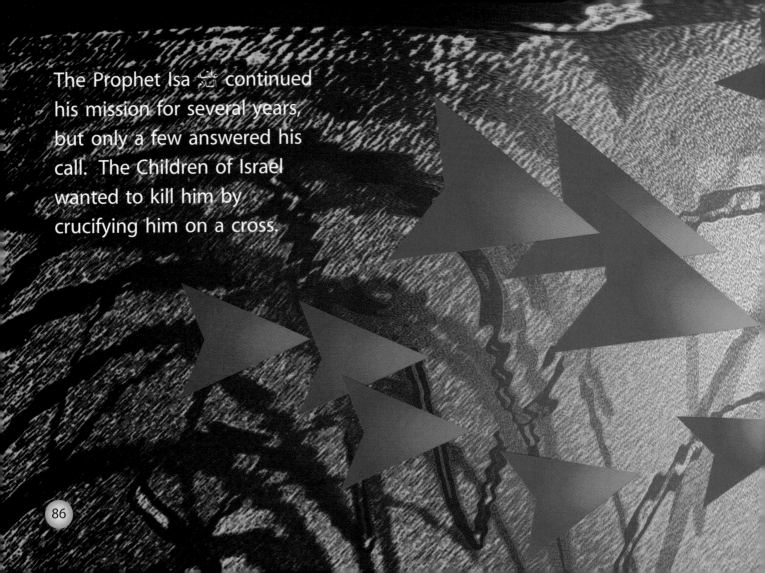

The Prophet Isa ﷺ continued his mission for several years, but only a few answered his call. The Children of Israel wanted to kill him by crucifying him on a cross.

But Allah saved him and they crucified another man who was made to appear like him.

The Prophet Isa ﷺ said that the scriptures which had been revealed earlier, were true, and told the people about the last Prophet.

Allah

Bles

an

...o, I am the servant of Allah;
...s given me the Book,
       and made me a Prophet.
...d He has made me, wherever I may be;
...d He has enjoined me to pray,
...o give the alms, so long as I live,
...and likewise to cherish my mother,
...as not made me arrogant, unprosperous.
...eace be upon me, the day I was born,
            and the day I die,
...d the day I am raised up alive!

— Surah Maryam
19:30-33

91

He said, 'I am sent forth to you from Allah to confirm the *Tawrat* already revealed, and to give you news of a messenger who will come after me whose name is Ahmed.'

The Prophet Isa عَلَيْهِ السَّلَام went up to
heaven from the town of Nasiriya.

There are sayings of the Prophet Muhammad ﷺ which tell of the return of the Prophet Isa عَلَيْهِ السَّلَام to the earth before the Day of Judgement.

Find Out More

To know more about the message and meaning of Allah's words, look up the following parts of the Quran which tell the story of the Prophet Isa ﷺ.

Surah al-Ma'idah 5:112-115

97

The Honoured Guests

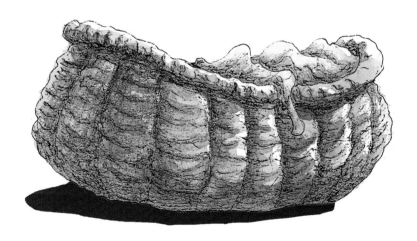

The Prophet Ibrahim or Abraham ﷺ was one of the great prophets. He lived in the land of Palestine.

The Prophet Ibrahim ﷺ continued his preaching about the oneness of Allah and the message of the Hereafter for a very long time. But none responded his call except his wife and nephew, whose name was Lut or Lot ﷺ. One day some angels came to the Prophet Ibrahim ﷺ in human form. The Prophet Ibrahim ﷺ did not recognise them.

103

When the angels entered the house of the Prophet Ibrahim عليه السلام, they said, "Peace! Peace!" The Prophet Ibrahim عليه السلام returned their greetings.

104

Seeing that they were strangers, the Prophet Ibrahim  rushed inside the house and brought a grilled calf for them. He placed it before them. But the angels did not touch the food.

Seeing that the strangers did not have the food, the Prophet Ibrahim ﷺ grew afraid of them. But they said, "Have no fear."

The angels gave him
good news of a son
who would become a
wise person.

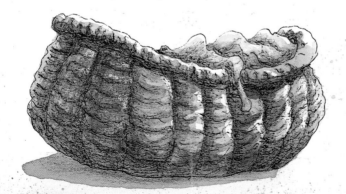

His wife did not believe the words of the angels and came crying and beating her face: "Surely, I am a barren old woman."

But the angels told her that "this is the will of your Lord, He is the Wise one, the All-Knowing." The Prophet Ibrahim عليه السلام asked the angels, "What is your errand?"

They said, "We have been sent forth to a wicked nation, so that we may bring down on them a shower of claystones marked by your Lord for the destruction of the sinful."

And so the angels destroyed the sinful people who used to live near the Dead Sea in those days.

115

Find Out More

To know more about the message and
meaning of Allah's words, look up the
following parts of the Quran which tells
the story of the Honoured Guests:
Surah al-Dhariyat 51:24-37

116

The Prophet Shuayb عليه السلام and the Earthquake

Long long ago, the people of Madyan and Ayka settled on the Arabian coast of the Red Sea.

119

The area, to the East of lower Egypt, extends westwards from the present-day Gulf of Aqaba deep into the Sinai Peninsula as far as the mountain of Moab, which lies to the east of the Dead Sea.

121

The people of Madyan and Ayka were at first the followers of the Prophet Ibrahim عليه السلام, but over the next 500 years they did wrong things, were dishonest and turned away from the true faith.

Then Allah sent the Prophet Shuayb عليه السلام to these erring people to show them the right path. He warned them to be honest in weights and measures, and not to trick others into giving away what was rightfully theirs.

The Prophet Shuayb ﷺ reminded them of the blessings which Allah had showered on them: "Remember how He multiplied you when you were few in number."

But the elders of his people rejected him, saying, "Shuayb, much of what you say we cannot understand. We know how weak you are in our midst." They threatened to "drive him out along with his followers" from their homeland.

The Prophet Shuayb ﷺ said, "I do not want to argue with you, for that would mean my doing what I forbid you to do. I am trying only to reform you as far as I am able. Nor can I succeed without Allah's help. In Him I have put my trust, and to Him I turn to say sorry for whatever I have done wrong."

His people replied that but for his tribe they would have stoned him. "My people", said Shuayb ﻋﻠﻴﻪ ﺍﻟﺴﻼﻡ, "have you more regard for my tribe than for Allah? Dare you turn your backs upon Him? My Lord knows about all your actions. Do what you will, my people, and so will I. You shall know who will be punished and held up to shame, and who is lying. Wait if you will: I too am waiting."

They were punished by an earthquake, and when morning came they were lying flat in their houses, as if those who drove away the Prophet Shuayb عليه السلام had never lived there.

"Those who treated Shuayb عليه السلام with contempt were themselves the losers."

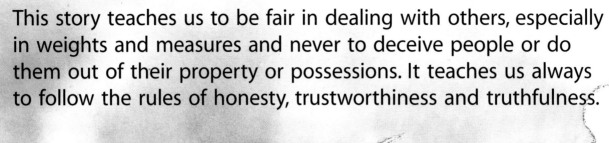

This story teaches us to be fair in dealing with others, especially in weights and measures and never to deceive people or do them out of their property or possessions. It teaches us always to follow the rules of honesty, trustworthiness and truthfulness.

Find Out More

To know more about the message and meaning of Allah's words, look up the following parts of the Quran which tells the story of the people of Madyan:

Surah al-Araf 7:85-93

Surah Hud 11:84-95

The Angel's Prayer

The angels are pure and noble beings created by Allah. They have been given special powers and qualities to carry out their duties assigned by Allah. Belief in the angels is part of the Islamic faith.

The angels are friends of the believers in this world and in the Hereafter. The Quran tells us that the angels were created even before human beings. They each have two, three or four pairs of wings.

The angels carry out the commands of Allah in total obedience. They are grouped in various categories.

Foremost among them is the Archangel Gabriel, or Jibril, who conveyed Allah's revelations to the prophets. It was Jibril who brought the revelation of the Quran to the Prophet Muhammad ﷺ.

143

Other important angels
are Mikail, or Mikhael, who
brings down the rain.

146

The angel Izrail or Azrael is given the task of carrying off human souls. He is also called *Malak al-Mawt*, or the Angel of Death.

One of them is known as Israfil. He is given the special task of blowing the Trumpet on the Last Day, when the earth will crumble to pieces at the sound of the Trumpet. Some of the angels are specially appointed to keep a watch on every person and record his or her every single good or bad deed.

The Prophet Muhammad ﷺ has said, that if someone tells a lie, due to its bad smell, the angels run several miles away from him. Therefore, we should not annoy them by doing any bad deeds.

On the Night of Power, or *Laylat al-Qadr,* which is one of the special nights of Ramadan, the angels come down on earth in greater numbers.

A number of angels carry the throne of Allah and stand around it. They give glory to the Lord and pray for the forgiveness of the faithful believers, saying:

"Lord, You embrace all things with Your mercy and Your knowledge. Forgive those that repent and follow Your path. Shield them from the scourge of Hell. Admit them, Lord, to the Garden of Eden which You have promised them, together with all the righteous among their fathers, their wives, and their descendants. You are the Almighty, the Wise One."

Find Out More
To know more about the message and meaning of
Allah's words, look up the following parts of the
Quran which tells the story of the angels:
    Surah Fatir 35:1
    Surah Ghafir 40:7-9

The Prophet and the Blind Man

The Prophet Muhammad ﷺ used to sit near the Kabah and explain passages from the Quran to people. One day as usual he was sitting near the Kabah and explaining the message of the Quran to some ungodly chiefs of the Quraysh tribe in the hope that they would listen to his message and accept Islam.

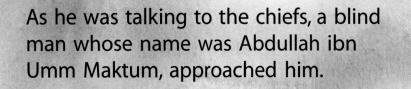

As he was talking to the chiefs, a blind man whose name was Abdullah ibn Umm Maktum, approached him.

162

The blind man did not realise that the Prophet was sitting with some high ranking people and was discussing some important matter with them.

As soon as the blind man approached the Prophet, he said, "O Messenger, teach me about whatever Allah has taught you."

The Prophet Muhammad ﷺ was annoyed at the blind man, cutting in like this and spoke roughly with him.

167

168

But Allah did not like the way the Prophet responded to the blind man, who had come to seek guidance from him. The following verses of the Quran were then revealed to the Prophet:

169

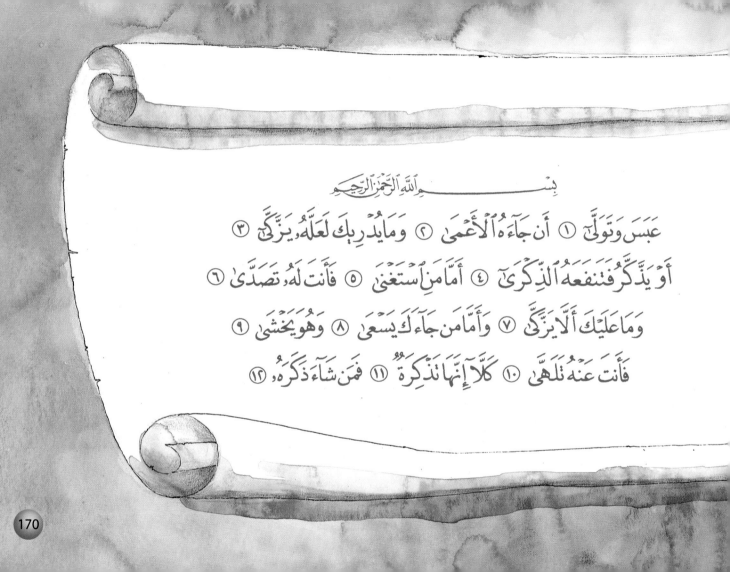

بِسْمِ اللَّهِ الرَّحْمَنِ الرَّحِيمِ

عَبَسَ وَتَوَلَّىٰ ۝ أَن جَاءَهُ الْأَعْمَىٰ ۝ وَمَا يُدْرِيكَ لَعَلَّهُ يَزَّكَّىٰ ۝

أَوْ يَذَّكَّرُ فَتَنفَعَهُ الذِّكْرَىٰ ۝ أَمَّا مَنِ اسْتَغْنَىٰ ۝ فَأَنتَ لَهُ تَصَدَّىٰ ۝

وَمَا عَلَيْكَ أَلَّا يَزَّكَّىٰ ۝ وَأَمَّا مَن جَاءَكَ يَسْعَىٰ ۝ وَهُوَ يَخْشَىٰ ۝

فَأَنتَ عَنْهُ تَلَهَّىٰ ۝ كَلَّا إِنَّهَا تَذْكِرَةٌ ۝ فَمَن شَاءَ ذَكَرَهُ ۝

170

When the blind man came to him, he (the Prophet)
gave him an angry look and turned his back on him.
Yet how do you know that he might purify himself?
Or be warned, and the warning may benefit him?
To one who was uncaring you were all attention,
although you do not have to ensure for it if he does not purify himself.
But one who comes to you eagerly and fearfully, you ignore.
No, indeed this (Quran) is a warning.
So, whoever is willing, let him seek remembrance from it.
(Surah Abasa, 80:1-12)

The Prophet Muhammad ﷺ later gave in, and treated Ibn Umm Maktum ever after with great respect, finally making him governor of Madinah.

172

173

The story of the blind man reminds us that no one in this world is superior to others, even if he has a high rank and position.

The message of this story is that one is only superior to another if he or she has a higher rank in the sight of the Lord.

Find Out More

To know more about the message and meaning of Allah's words, look up the following parts of the Quran which tell the story of the blind man.

Surah Abasa 80:1-12

The Traveller's Prayers

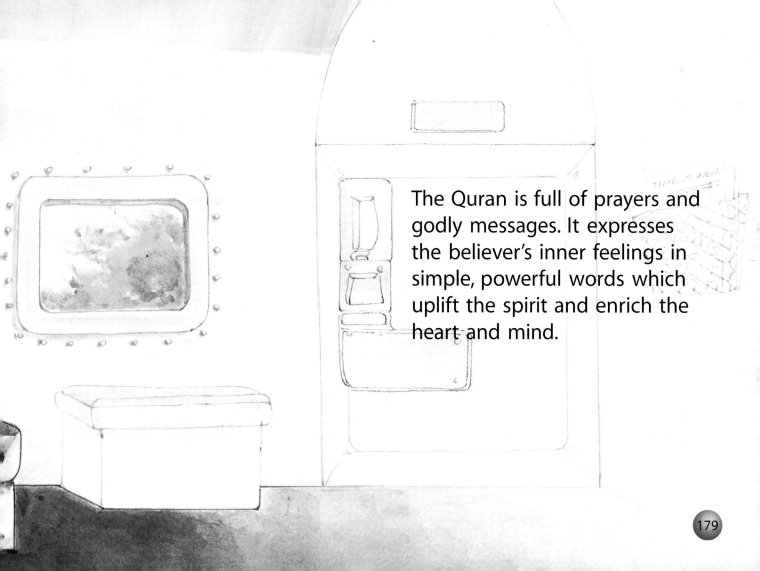

The Quran is full of prayers and godly messages. It expresses the believer's inner feelings in simple, powerful words which uplift the spirit and enrich the heart and mind.

179

The Quran reminds us to say our prayers while on a journey:

"It is He who made the earth a resting place...created all things in pairs and made for you the ships and beasts on which you ride, so that you may remember your Lord's blessing when you are seated on them."

Therefore, the Prophet Muhammad ﷺ would often recite the following prayer while riding a camel or a horse: *"Glory be to Him, who has made these (animals) serve us, for we ourselves could not be their masters. To our Lord we shall all return."*

This prayer reminds us that all means of going from one place to another, whether animals such as horses or camels, or machines such as cars, aeroplanes or ships, are actually a blessing from the Almighty.

With the help of the forces in nature that the Creator has given, we are able to make them work. For example, cars run on petrol or gas, which has been created by the Almighty. Without this we could not use them.

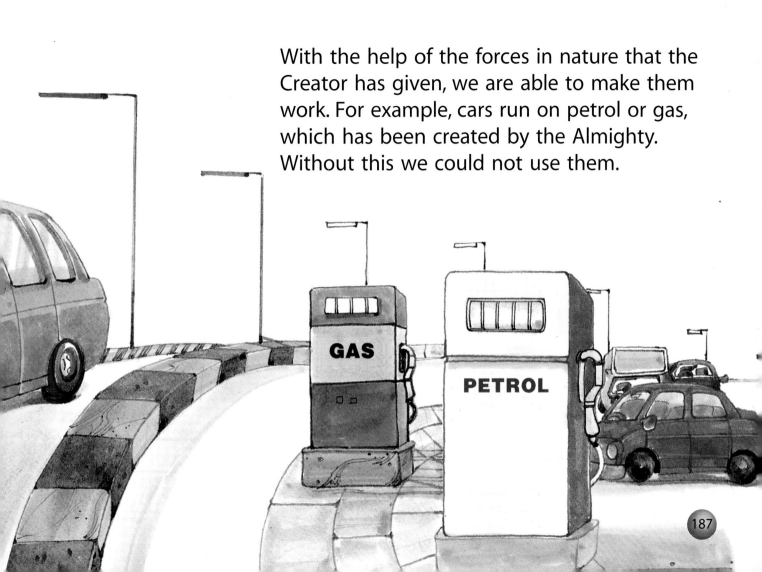

Similarly, aeroplanes fly in the sky, thanks to a kind of force found in the air. Without this force, no aeroplanes could fly.

We should thank Allah for all these blessings with a sense of awe, as man could not do anything if the Creator had not provided all the natural resources which we use.

Therefore, whenever we sit in a car or on board a ship we should recite the traveller's prayer. This shows that we realise that all the things that we possess are blessings from the Almighty, our Creator.

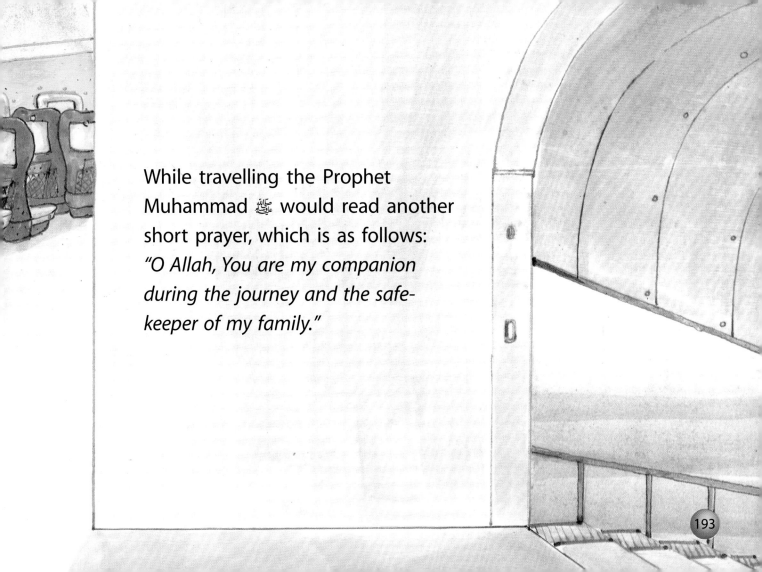

While travelling the Prophet Muhammad ﷺ would read another short prayer, which is as follows: *"O Allah, You are my companion during the journey and the safe-keeper of my family."*

سُبْحَانَ الَّذِىْ سَخَّرَ لَنَا هٰذَا وَمَا كُنَّا لَهٗ

مُقْرِنِيْنَ وَ اِنَّا اِلٰى رَبِّنَا لَمُنْقَلِبُوْنَ

Subhan alladhi sakhkhara-lana hadha, wa ma
kunna lahu muqrineena wa inna ila rabbina la munqaliboon.

Glory be to Him, who has made these serve us,
for we ourselves could not be their masters.
To our Lord we shall all return.

194

اَللّٰهُمَّ اَنْتَ الصَّاحِبُ فِی السَّفَرِ،
وَ الْخَلِيفَةُ فِی الْاَهْلِ

Allahumma antas-sahibu fis-safar,
wal khalifatu fil-ahl.

*O Allah, You are my companion during
the journey and the safe keeper of my family.*

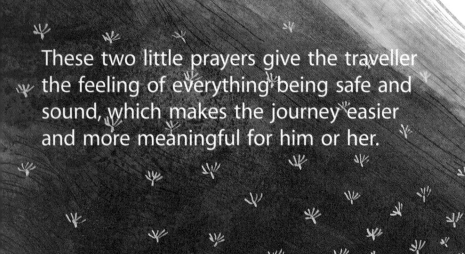

These two little prayers give the traveller the feeling of everything being safe and sound, which makes the journey easier and more meaningful for him or her.

Find Out More

To know more about the message and meaning of Allah's words, look up the following parts of the Quran which tells about the traveller's prayer.

Surah al-Zukhruf 43:14

The Rivers of
Milk and Honey

Believers are promised by Allah that they will be given Paradise in the life after death. It shall be the greatest gift from their Lord for their good actions and their bowing to the will of their Creator at all times. Paradise will be given to those fortunate people who live good lives on earth.

199

The Quran tells us in great detail what Paradise will look like and who will be the people to live in its lush green gardens. The praises of Allah will be sung on all sides in the gardens of Paradise. Only those who praise the Lord on earth will be fit to enter such a heaven. But how can one be fit to enter Paradise if one thinks of oneself or others as being great?

The true believer is a flower of the garden of Paradise. It sprouts in this world and blossoms in the Hereafter. Paradise will be a place full of right actions. Only those who think rightly on earth will be able to enter such a heaven. Those who do bad deeds which cause ruin in this world cannot hope to enter Paradise. Only those who stop themselves from doing vain and base things will be allowed to enter the heavenly home of Paradise.

Therefore, try your best for your Lord's pardon, and for a Paradise as vast as the heaven and earth which was made for those who believe in Allah and His prophets.

On the Last Day the angel Jibril and many other angels will stand up in their ranks. They will not speak unless their Lord permits. There shall be no idle talk, no lies, no sinful speech— only the greeting, "Peace! Peace!"

The people of Paradise shall be served with silver dishes, and cups as large as goblets; silver goblets which they themselves shall measure: and cups filled to the top with ginger-flavoured water from a fountain called Salsabil. They shall be attended by boys who will always be young, who to the one who looks on will seem like sprinkled pearls. When you gaze upon that scene, you will see a kingdom full of happiness and glory.

The people of Paradise shall rest on jewelled couches and carpets richly spread. Trees will spread their shade around them, and fruits such as dates and pomegranates will hang in bunches over them. Rivers will flow through the gardens, the fruits of which will all be within their reach.

The people of Paradise shall wear in garments of fine green silk and rich brocade, and have bracelets of silver on their arms. Their Lord will give them pure nectar to drink. And theirs shall be the dark-eyed houris, chaste as hidden pearls.

This is the Paradise which good people have been promised. There shall flow rivers of the purest water, and rivers of the clearest honey, rivers of milk forever fresh, and rivers of wine tasting sweet to those who drink it. (Such wine will neither hurt their heads nor take away their reason).

But the most blessed and thrilling thing to happen in Paradise will be meeting with the Lord Himself—a face to face meeting. And the Lord will say to His good righteous servants:

"O soul at peace!
Return to your Lord, joyful,
and pleasing in His sight.
Join My servants and
enter My Paradise."

Find Out More

To know more about the message and meaning of Allah's
words, look up the following parts of the Quran which
tells the story of the Rivers of Milk and Honey:

Surah Muhammad 47:15
Surah at-Tur 52:20
Surah Rahman 55:46-78
Surah al-Waqiah 56:11-26
Surah al-Fajr 89:27-30

Ramadan and the Quran

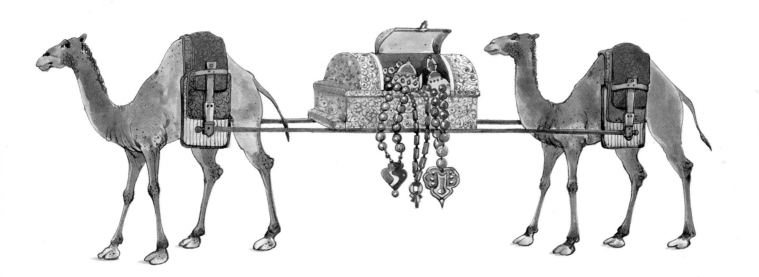

The Prophet Muhammad ﷺ would often sit alone in the cave of Hira, near Makkah, to pray and think deeply, asking the Creator of the Heavens and earth for answers to the questions that surged through his mind.

What is man's true role in life? What does the Lord require of us? From where does man come, and where will he go after death? All alone the Prophet would remain deep in thought, surrounded by nature, seeking answers to all these profound questions.

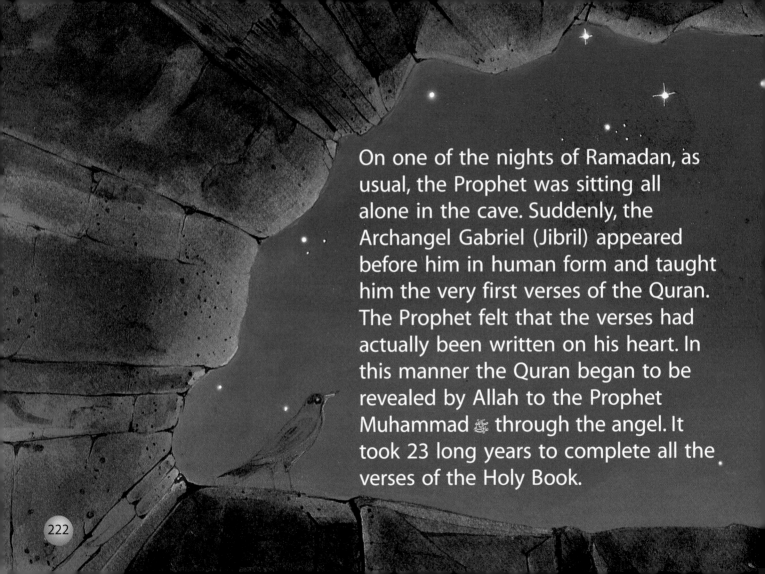

On one of the nights of Ramadan, as usual, the Prophet was sitting all alone in the cave. Suddenly, the Archangel Gabriel (Jibril) appeared before him in human form and taught him the very first verses of the Quran. The Prophet felt that the verses had actually been written on his heart. In this manner the Quran began to be revealed by Allah to the Prophet Muhammad ﷺ through the angel. It took 23 long years to complete all the verses of the Holy Book.

Being the true word of
Allah in human language,
the Quran is a book of
learning for all mankind
which will last forever.

225

It provides correct and understandable answers to all the central questions which arise in a mind which seeks answers. It serves as a guiding light, inspiring and leading the devout on the right path. The guidance given in the Quran is one of a kind and a great blessing to mankind from Allah, because it shows man the path to final success. It tells man how to behave, so that in the life after death he may enter Paradise, which is the final goal. Fasting is the path to it.

The month of Ramadan, therefore, is a yearly reminder of this blessing which has no equal.

The celebration of the revelation of the Quran is not observed in the usual way, but is marked by not eating and drinking, and by showing gratitude to the Almighty, by various forms of charity. Fasting in this month is like saying 'Thank You' for the divine blessing.

229

This month is the very best one for reading and understanding the Quran. Special recitations of the Quran are held; it is also recited during the *tarawih* prayer.

The *tarawih* is actually the *tahajjud* prayer, which instead of being offered before dawn is offered after the *isha* prayer during this month to make things easy for godly people.

The Quran introduces the Creator and explains the bond between the Creator and His creations. A large part of the Quran deals with stories of the prophets, such as Adam, Nuh (Noah), Ibrahim (Abraham), Yusuf (Joseph), Musa (Moses), Isa (Jesus) and many more, upon all of whom be peace. These stories teach lessons about what is good or bad for believers of all time.

Another part of the Quran talks about the Hereafter—which mainly describes in detail the delights of Paradise and the agony of Hell. Historical events, faith and religion, religious commandments, divine promises, prayers and matters of civil law are also dealt with.

When the Quran is read during the month of its revelation, Ramadan, it creates an atmosphere which reminds us of the time when the divine light from heaven fell upon the earth. The Quran is a guiding force in man's life. He earns his livelihood according to its rules. He bathes in the ocean of its life to cleanse his soul.

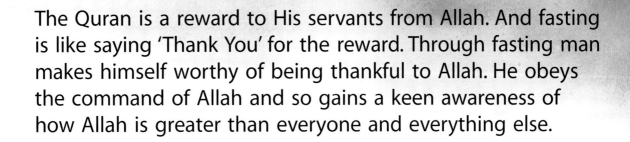

The Quran is a reward to His servants from Allah. And fasting is like saying 'Thank You' for the reward. Through fasting man makes himself worthy of being thankful to Allah. He obeys the command of Allah and so gains a keen awareness of how Allah is greater than everyone and everything else.

Having gone through a month's fasting, the believer is then able to lead a life of piety as laid down in the Qur'an.

Find Out More

To know more about the message and meaning of Allah's words, look up the following parts of the Quran which tells the story of Ramadan.

Surah al-Baqarah 2:183-185

Surah al-Alaq 96:1-5

Where to find the stories in the Quran

Help your Child understand the stories from the Quran

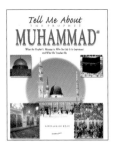

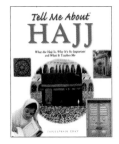

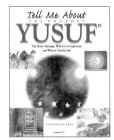

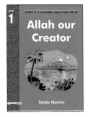

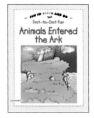

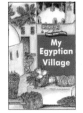

GIFT BOXES

A Fun Way to Learn About the Quran

goodwordbooks.com